MW00892006

May 15, 2015

Norah Rue –

This is a really special book for several reason! You are already a beautiful girl. Your Moms know how important it is for you to know you are smart, kind to others, brave, kind to yourself, and talented.

Your Mama knows Lena's grandmother. She is one of my dearest friends. Lena is a real little girl just like you! Her Mom knows Lena is beautiful just like you are beautiful, Norah Rue!

I will love you always!

Mama

Is Lena Pretty?

Written and Illustrated by Liza Dora

Edited by Jolie Gray

Through every struggle I've had,
every doubt and fear,
it was you pushing me on.
Urging me forward and
ever-so-quietly telling me to try.

Because one day we would meet,
and forever you would be mine.

For Lena

A special thanks to
Jolie Gray, Crystal Johnson, Michelle Underwood and Amanda Fullilove
for sharing a dream with me.

ISBN: 978-0-692-43392-8

Lena has eyes that are
blue like the sky.

Her hair twists into
dark curls that people
love to touch.

“What a pretty girl,”
they all say.

At the grocery store,
Lena helps Daddy pick
out all the vegetables.

She knows the names
and colors of every one.

Four red tomatoes,
one purple eggplant,
five orange carrots,
and twelve little,
green Brussels sprouts.

Daddy tells Lena
she's smart.

At home, Lena helps Momma wash the dishes. She dries the dishes carefully with a towel and...

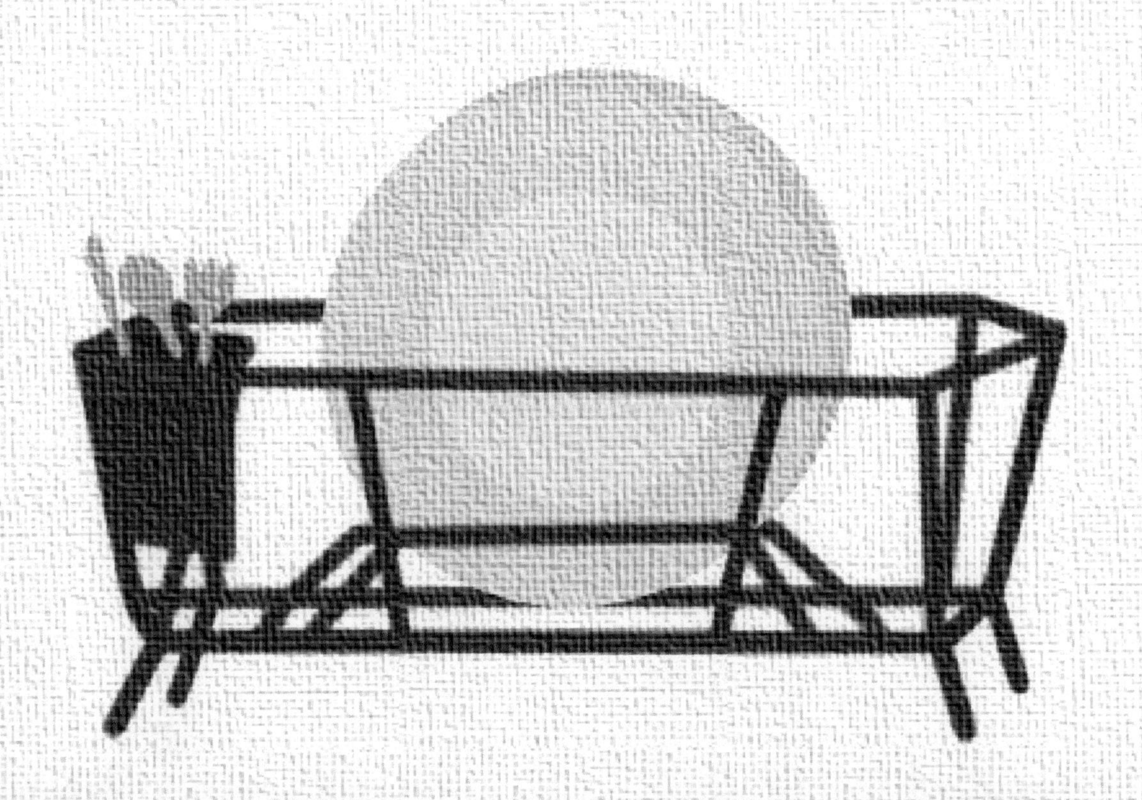

...then puts them away in
their proper cabinet.

Momma tells Lena she's
helpful.

At school, a new girl
named Myra joins
Lena's class.

Lena shares her toys
with Myra.

Lena sits with Myra at lunch.
Her teacher, Ms. Roberts, tells
Lena she's kind.

Papi picks Lena up from school.

On the way home, they listen to the radio and sing. Lena knows all the words to the song.

She sings the loud parts LOUD and the soft parts soft.

Papi tells Lena she's talented.

Sarah, Lena's favorite babysitter, comes over after school. Sarah and Lena read books and play games, but Sarah accidentally rolls Lena's favorite ball underneath the bed.

Sarah says when she was little, she was scared there might be monsters underneath her bed, but Lena isn't scared.

Lena lifts the bed skirt and grabs the ball. Sarah says Lena is brave.

Daddy and Momma come in to kiss Lena goodnight.

"Momma," says Lena, "Am I pretty?"

Momma sits down on Lena's bed.

"Why do you ask?"

"Well, Daddy says I'm smart, you said I'm helpful, Ms. Roberts said I'm kind, Papi said I'm talented and Sarah said I'm brave."

Momma smiles. “If I told you someone was smart, helpful, kind, talented and brave, would you think they were pretty?”

Lena thinks for a minute before she answers: “I’d think they were beautiful”.

Momma kisses Lena
on the forehead.
“Then, my darling,
Lena is
beautiful.”

CPSIA information can be obtained
at www.ICGtesting.com
Printed in the USA
LVIC04*1121300415
436728LV00013B/43

J 782.0096 S698 2011

CCL

SONGS FROM THE BAOBAB

AFRICAN LULLABIES & NURSERY RHYMES

Songs collected by Chantal Grosléziat
Musical arrangements by Paul Mindy
Illustrations by Élodie Nouhen

Dallas Public Library

1 Uélé molibá mákási CONGO

The current is very strong . . . row, row

2 Ka baga ne ma MALI

One, two, three . . .
the mother of triplets is tired

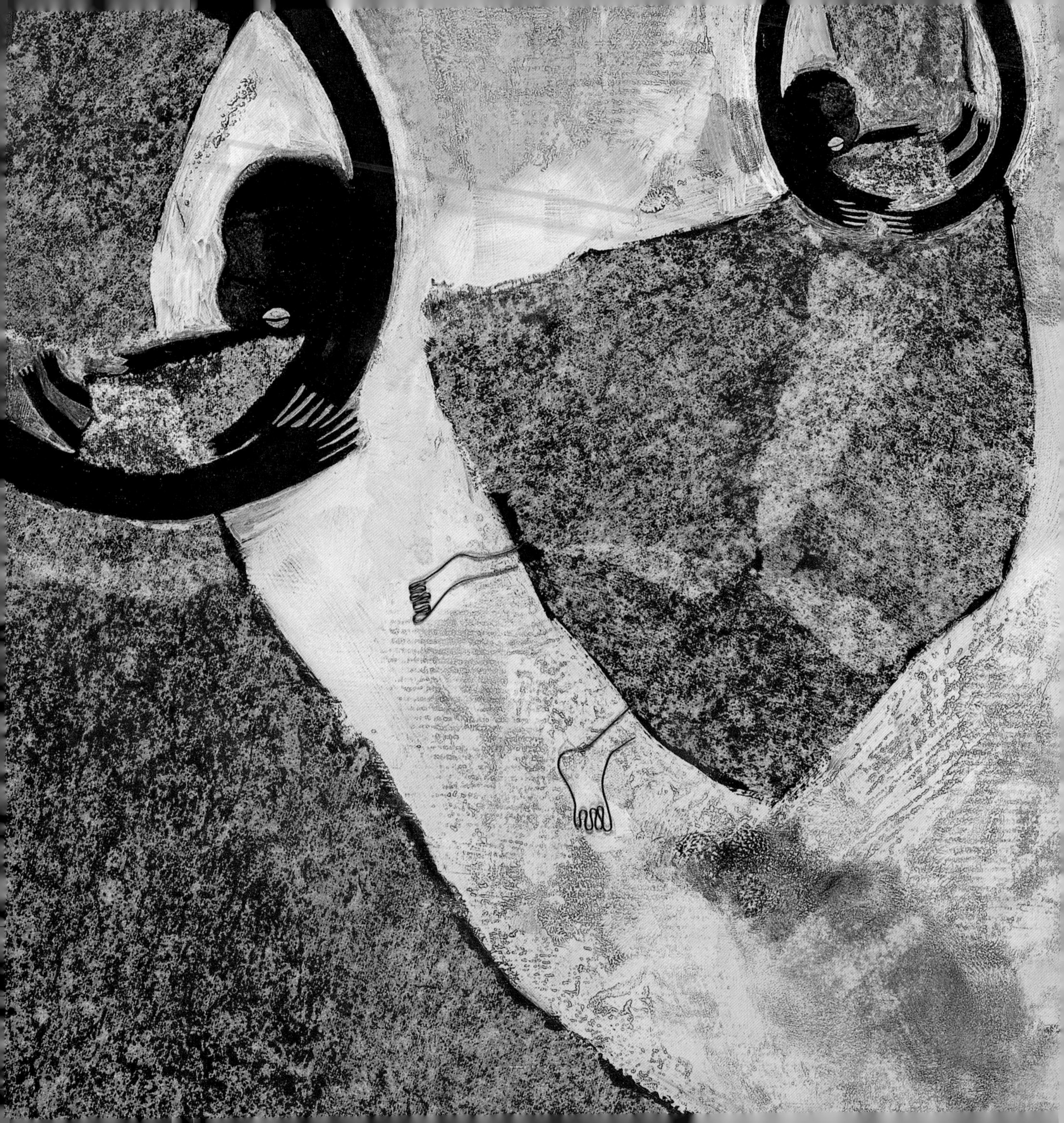

3 Ndi le e CAMEROON

When it rains,
when it shines . . .
sleep baby sleep

4 So diyara IVORY COAST

Your arrival brought joy . . . to the house

5 Yum-maa yehii jaaɓe MAURITANIA

Your mother has gone to the bush . . .
to look for jujubes

6 Eya bé TOGO

This one says . . .
the thumb is a tattletale

7 Baranin IVORY COAST

That one says . . .
the unripe orange gives no juice

8 Mademba SENEGAL

My child . . . my beloved

9 Aayóo nenne! SENEGAL
Sleep baby . . . pretty baby

10 Denko IVORY COAST
Tell me what could be more important . . .
show me

11 Nwou wo' lâ nzi ntâ nseu? CAMEROON

Our child is walking . . . since when?

12 Kabuye kanjye RWANDA

Hold the little pebble . . . my little pebble

13 Nkwihoreze RWANDA

I will comfort you . . .
I will give you milk

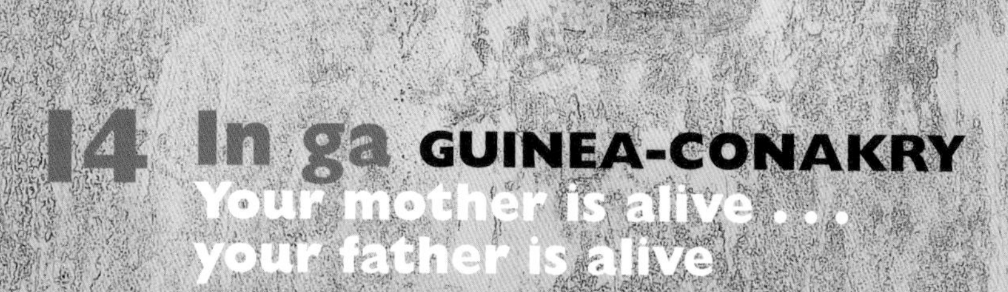

14 In ga GUINEA-CONAKRY

Your mother is alive . . .
your father is alive

15 Faatima Hawwaa MAURITANIA

Losing your mother is unlucky . . .
losing your father even more so

16 Makun MALI

**Baby is hungry . . .
don't cry, there's nothing wrong**

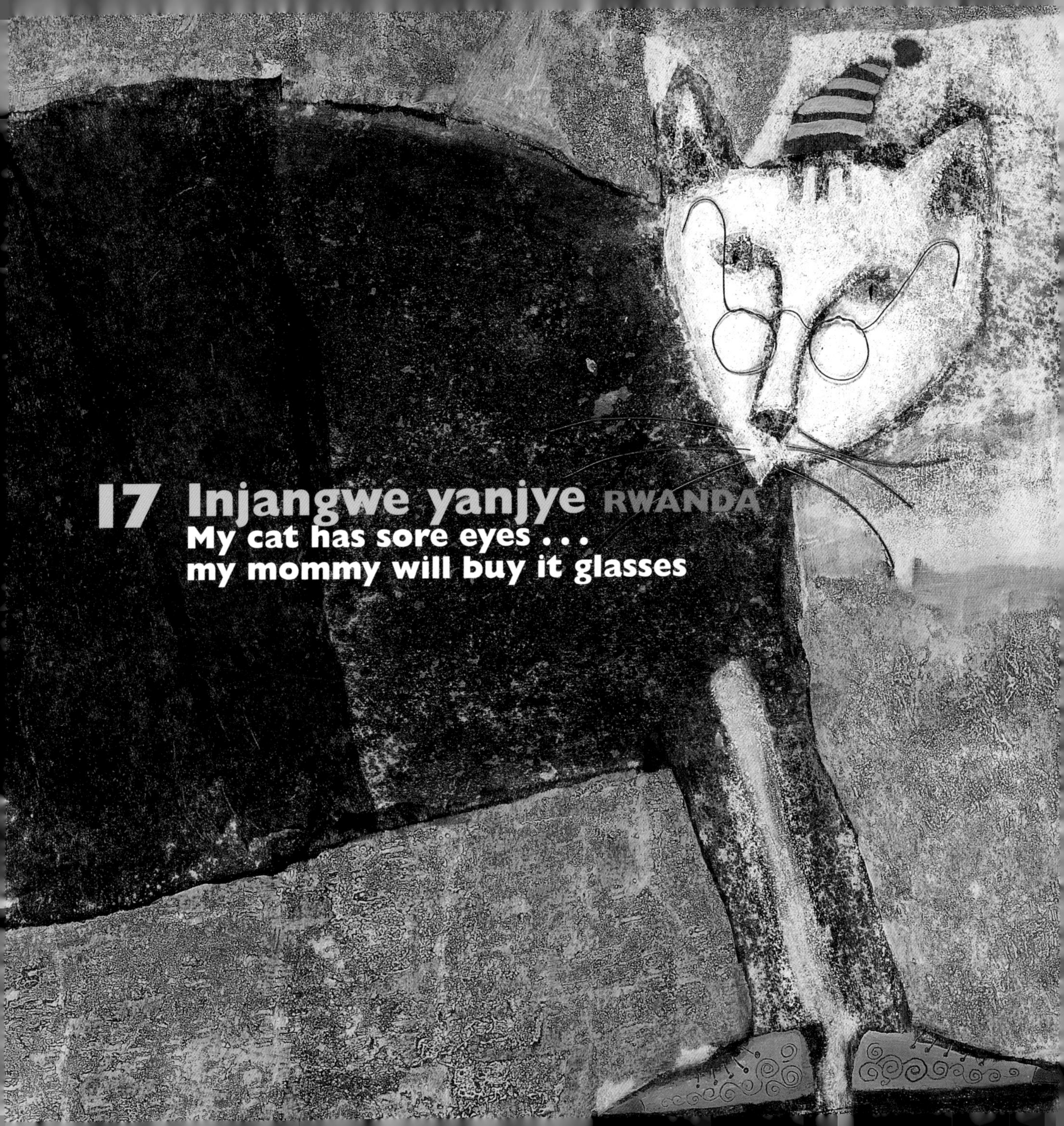

17 Injangwe yanjye RWANDA

My cat has sore eyes . . .
my mommy will buy it glasses

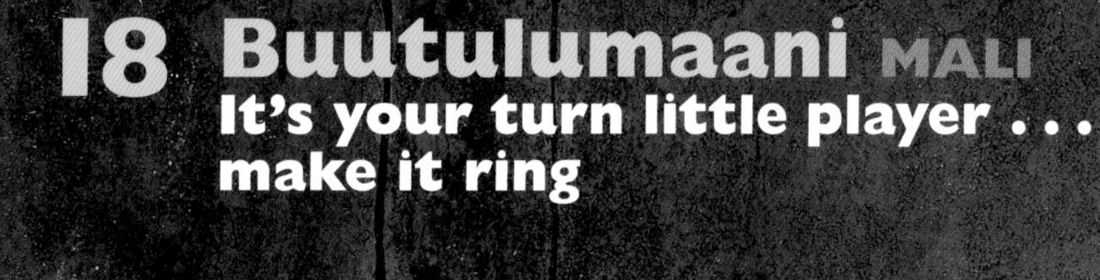

18 Buutulumaani MALI
It's your turn little player . . . make it ring

19 Sirada la MALI
I headed down the roadside . . . I told it to sing

20 Tànk loxo nopp SENEGAL

Nose, neck, eye, mouth . . . shh!

21 N daga an kara MALI

Pit, pat, the fat cat . . .
in and out, the little mouse

22 Tutu gbo̱vi TOGO

Stop crying my dear . . . spit it out

23 Îtä Zâke CENTRAL AFRICAN REPUBLIC

Morning bells are ringing . . . wake up

Awe bebëe! CENTRAL AFRICAN REPUBLIC

**Mommy has gone to the river . . .
she'll be back soon**

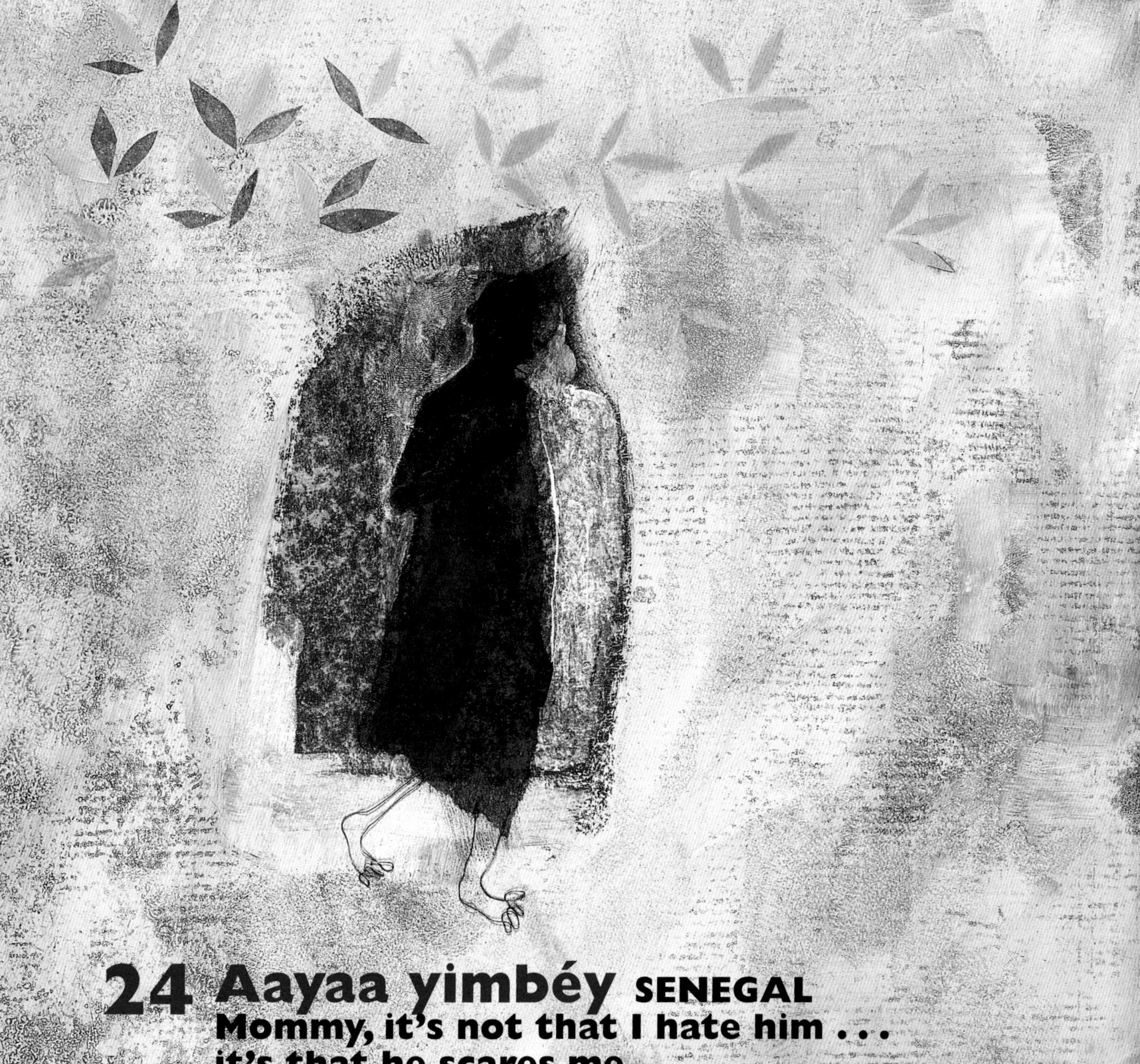

24 Aayaa yimbéy SENEGAL

Mommy, it's not that I hate him . . .
it's that he scares me

25 Bo bo bo bo GUINEA-CONAKRY

You cry for milk . . .
but I don't have any to give

26 Dunga CENTRAL AFRICAN REPUBLIC

The day you came to our house . . .
I became your mother

27 Usumani ka dundunnin MALI
Beat the drum . . . Africa is waiting for you

28 Gato gato RWANDA

**She is a beautiful gazelle . . .
the prettiest girl of all**

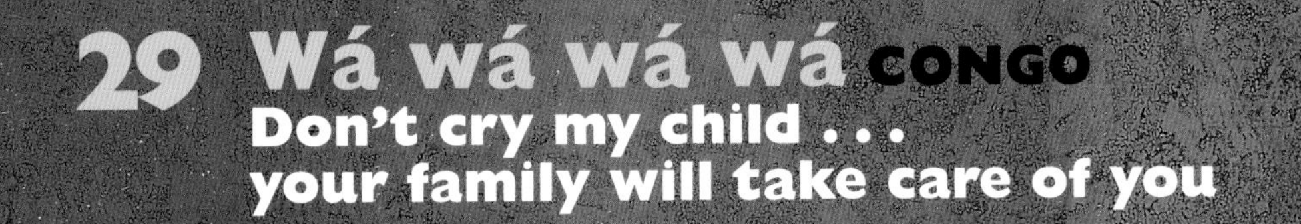

29 Wá wá wá wá CONGO

Don't cry my child . . . your family will take care of you

1 Uélé molibá mákási CONGO
(Uélé, river with a very strong current)

Singers **Jean-Marie Bolangassa, Marie-Cécile Maloumbi Mata, Uriel Koukou Cissoko, Anaïs Mwinda Mata, Clarisse Mata** and **Emmanuel Victor Mata** Language **Lingala**

olélé olélé molibá mákási	Olélé! Olélé! The current is very strong
lúká lúká	Row! Row!
mbôká ná yé	His country
mbôká mbôká Kásáï	His country is Kasaï
eeo ee eeo Béngúélà áyá	Éeo, éé éeo, let Benguela come!
óyá óyá	Come! Come!
Yákárá a	The brave one
óyá óyá	Come! Come!
Kóngúidjá a	The generous one
óyá óyá	Come! Come!

This song comes from a folk tale: fishermen come back empty-handed. They need to find a new fishing spot. In order to ensure a better fate for themselves they involve the spirits of a river that is filled with fish, the Kasaï River, and sing to implore the water spirits. When the current is very powerful and they have to row hard, they praise the chief of the region, Benguela, who acts as their intermediary with the ancestors. This masculine song, an incantation and song of praise, is also included in the children's repertory. Through it, they are introduced to the work of fishing and can entertain themselves by rocking and mimicking the fishermen. But, like many sailors' songs, its renown has long extended beyond borders, as witnessed by the fact that it appears in *Tintin in the Congo* (*Tintin au Congo*) in 1946.

2 Ka baga ne ma **MALI (Don't provoke me)**

Singers **Sylla Mama** and **Niama Kouyate** Language **Bambara**

ka baga ne ma nyɛ bɔ n' nyɛrɔ
ne cɛ natɔ kana an sɔrɔ kuma la
wɛrɛ wɛrɛ siri wawa siri siri siri wawa
polisicɛ i bolo bɔ n kan na
ne cɛ natɛ a kana an sɔrɔ kuma la
wɛrɛ siri wawa siri siri siri wawa
kelen n'an ye waa kelen dugu la
fila n'an ye waa fila dugu la
saba sabaninw ba sɛgɛnna
naani mɔgɔ tɛ mɔgɔ neni gansan
duuru lon bɛ na setuma don
wɔɔrɔ, woro ci gansan i bolo bila yɛrɛwolo la ye
Wolonfila, muso bɛna wolonya le
seegin sennamaa ye gɛlɛman
kɔnɔntɔ kɔnɔ bɛna pancogo don
tan cɛ bɛna den tan sɔrɔ
Arama Siriki na den tan sɔrɔ
O y'a fɔ le n'in baw kɛlɛlen

Don't provoke me, I'm ignoring you
My husband is coming; I don't want him to see me talking to you
Don't put your arm around my neck, Mr. Officer!
My husband is coming; I don't want him to see me talking to you
One, come with me to the country of the lonely!
Two, come with me to the land of the saba
Three, the mother of triplets is tired
Four, don't insult people without cause
Five, the sun rises each day as usual
Six, opening the cola for no reason, raising your hand to a legitimate child
Seven, each woman gives birth in her own way
Eight, it's hard to surprise pedestrians
Nine, each bird flies in its own way
Ten, a man will have ten children
Adama Sidiki had ten children
He said I don't get along with my mothers
He said I don't get along with my fathers

This very catchy song comes from the tradition of dancing songs. Little girls sing it while standing in a circle and clapping their hands; one of them moves to the middle of the circle and starts to dance. It is a surprising blend of a vaudeville-like song that talks about seduction, and a nursery rhyme that goes through the numbers from one to ten, with word plays, rhythms and rhymes whose essence cannot be fully translated, and associates them with short proverbs of typical African wisdom. As in the case of all nursery rhymes, there are several versions of this one. It should be noted that the singer did not sing the verse concerning the number seven.

3 Ndi le e CAMEROON (Sleep)

Singer Ghislaine Noupa Language Bamana

mbâ' mben meu ndou
mpou meu nguêh : ndo nwou ngâ dieuh
mbâ' nep meu thieu
mpou meu nguêh : ndo nwou ngâ dieuh
tâ tâ kou ngan nseuh
woh meu ngo mbou le
ndi le e ndi le e bebe
ndi le e ndi le e Daniela

When it rains
They tell me to take the child inside
When the sun shines
They tell me to take the child inside
The chiefdom guardian is walking around the village:
"Who is making the child cry?"
Sleep, sleep baby!
Sleep, sleep Daniela!

Bamana is a language used in western Cameroon, below Foumban. Originating from Bangante, it is so diversified that the language is different from one village to another. But people do understand one another and many variations of this lullaby are found in all of the languages used in the region. It is not uncommon for the women to sing this song, in a group of several people, when they get together to assist the young mother, particularly during the child's first three years. This lullaby provides a marvellous illustration of the importance of community in Africa. At any time, in the village, a child can be cared for by the entire group. Kou Ngan, the head of the chiefdom, is the invisible guardian of the village.

In African tradition, when calming a baby, it is common to hold the child close to one's body, while rocking him or even shaking him quickly. This is a civilization in which babies are carried rather than placed in a cradle. It therefore comes as no surprise to hear lullabies as quick and as lively as this one. The recording features a berimbau, a descendant of the musical bow that may have come from the hunting bow. The musician rhythmically strikes the string with a stick and obtains different resonances by pressing the opening of the half gourd against his chest. The sound is modulated by the tension on the bow.

4 So diyara IVORY COAST (The joyful house)

Singers Sagna Guire Ramata and Niama Kouyate Language Bambara

alu nakan de
alu nakan de so diyara
alu nakan de
denbaw nakan de sodiyara
ka wari di dɔlu ma
ka sanu di dɔlu ma
dɔlu bololankolon bɛ

The announcement of your arrival
The announcement of your arrival brought joy to the house
Just the announcement of your arrival
The arrival of the mothers brought joy to the house
To some, we give money
To others, we give gold
The third ones, they leave empty-handed

This song, which is also very well known in Mali, celebrates marriage. The various mothers in attendance on the bride's side (bride's mother and aunts, mother's friends) sing until they reach the groom's house, accompanied by a griotte—the guardian of the oral tradition and the person responsible at this time for praising the families' worth—and occasionally by a percussionist with his drum. In this version, an allusion is made to the money paid by the groom's family as a dowry. It also contains a denunciation of injustice and a call for more equality among the children. It is not rare to hear little girls, aged seven or eight, singing this song and including it in their games.

The introduction and the accompaniment for the song on the recording are performed on the sanza, an instrument made of metal blades fixed to a wooden plank or box. It is played with the thumbs; earning it the nickname "thumb piano".

5 Yum-maa yehii jaaɓe MAURITANIA (Your mother has gone to search for jujubes)

Singer **Haby Sy** Language **Fula**

Yum-maa yehii jaaɓe	Your mother has gone to the bush to look for jujubes
– OO baynaa! OO baynaa!	– Ô, baynâ! Ô, baynâ!
Deyyu, Deyyu, Deyyu	Be quiet. Don't cry!
O addii jaaɓel gootel	She only found one
Muccii e hakkunde laawol	She ate it on her way back
Ferlii e hakkunde maayo	She threw the pit in the river
Deyyu, Deyyu, Deyyu	Be quiet. Don't cry!

It is traditionally the children who pick the jujubes, a fruit that is smaller and harder than the cherry. The mother, who leaves to go and eat these fruits in hiding, is really behaving like a child! By throwing the pit into the river, she is trying to erase any trace of her action and, who knows, maybe concealing another secret . . . A shepherd's reed flute accompanies the singer's voice with harmonic sounds on the recording. At the beginning of each phrase, the singer makes an "ouou" sound that she varies with a lateral movement of her tongue. This serves to draw the baby's attention as a rattle would.

6 Eya bé TOGO (He says)

Singers **Lucie Da Silvera, James Da Silvera** and **Tracy Da Silvera** Language **Mina**

eya bé niè niè	This one says, "Waa! Waa!" (little finger)
eya bé nukèyé lé wowo	This one asks, "What's wrong with him?" (ring finger)
eya bé ado yé lé wui	This one says, "He's hungry." (middle finger)
eya bé wo lé wozémé	This one says, "There is flour in the flour bin." (index finger)
eya bé dè mia du	And adds, "Make us something to eat!" (index finger)
eya bé dada gbó ma toé né	This one says, "I'm gonna tell Mommy when she comes home." (thumb)
déglé fosu sa sakplé	The thumb is a tattletale! (ring, middle and index fingers)

Mina is a dialect spoken by the Guins, who originally came from Elmina (Ghana) and settled in the southern coastal region of Togo. Children enjoy this finger game up until primary school. Why are there six phrases for five fingers? In order to maintain the rhythm of the game, the index finger speaks twice. The song has several themes: solidarity among children, the value of giving your word and of secrets, defiance . . . A small drama of daily life recounted in a few sentences.

7 Baranin IVORY COAST (Little gourde)

Singers **Sagna Guire Ramata** and **Niama Kouyate** Language **Bambara**

yowu yowu baranin yo, baranin yowu yowu
n tagara kungo la
ka taga damɛlɛkɛ sigilen sɔro
damɛlɛkɛ y'i kanto
lemuru kɔkɔbali ji tɛ bɔ
n sera n bolo ma se
lemuru kɔkɔbali ji tɛ bɔ

You, little extraordinary gourd!
I went into the bush
And saw an angel sitting
The angel said to me:
"The unripe orange gives no juice"
I arrived, but my hand was not there
"The unripe orange gives no juice"

This game, played by children during recess, requires a lot of coordination and rhythm. Positioned face to face, the children tap their hands against thei partner's (right hand at the top against the right hand, left hand at the bottom against the left hand, then the opposite). They have to go faster and faste and the first one to make a mistake is eliminated. The very poetic words of this nursery rhyme evoke the universe of the bush, where all invisible being live. The angel announces a prediction, using an enigmatic formula that resembles a saying. Its meaning is hidden and can be interpreted in many ways b the person who receives the message. The same applies to the final proverb, which is very common, and which could be explained as follows: "I have a the shapes, I have the appearance, but I'm not ready yet." An incitement to patience for children and adolescents . . .

8 Mademba SENEGAL

Singer **Souleymane Mbodj** Language **Wolof**

ku laal Mademba?
Sagar nga sa Naat yande
ku laal?
ndaat saay!
ku laal sama doom jee?
aayóo, xalaat, wéet te jooy oo
sama doom! sama soppe!
dund a mata ñaan oo
moom laay ñaan si Yàlla
ku laal sama doom jee?
aayóo, mane xalaat, wéet te jooy oo
wolloo, wolloo!

Who touched Mademba?
The rag, at Naat-yande
Who touched him?
What joy! Who touched my child?
I'm sad, I'm alone and I'm weeping
My child! My beloved!
Life alone deserves prayer
And that's what I am asking God
Who touched my child?
I'm sad, I'm alone and I'm weeping
Help, help!

This song denounces the intolerance that may be experienced by certain children in Africa. It is the story of Mademba, a little boy who is abandoned b his mother because he is illegitimate. The child was placed at the well near Naat-yande to be found. He is also called Sagar, which means rag, in order t be protected from death. A real name would attract attention to the child. According to the legend, a sparrowhawk takes the child and raises him. Th boy is told to sing the beginning of the song as often as he can. The day someone responds, that person will be his mother. This lullaby is therefore at th crossroads of story and reality. Today, the mothers sing it, without necessarily making the connection with the legend, to express both sadness and grea hope. The mother sacrifices herself for her child, who in turn will ensure her future, a sense of accountability that is instilled in African education very earl on. It should be noted that, in the most common version of this lullaby, the focus is simply on the joy of having a child and caressing it.

9 Aayóo nenne! SENEGAL (Sleep baby!)

Singer **Aminata Seck** Language **Wolof**

aayóo nenne!
ku may bindal téere
yóbbul ma ko Saalum?
Saalum, ñaari néeg la
ñetteel ba di waañ wa.
waañ wa waañu buur la
aayóo nenne!
nenne tuuti

Sleep, baby!
Who will make me a talisman?
And bring it to me in Saloum?
In Saloum, there are two bedrooms
The third room is the kitchen
And, it's the king's kitchen
Sleep, baby! Pretty baby!

Occasionally sung to another melody, this lullaby, which is very widespread in Senegal, is extremely soothing. Some versions also contain a first verse: I will send the person who touches my child to Saloum (region in southern Dakar). The song is about a talisman and the rejection of anything that could harm the child. The custom of offering a talisman to a baby to protect it against all evil is still very widespread. Most often, it is a verse from the Koran that is folded and wrapped in a leather pouch decorated with pearls and then tied around the baby's waist or neck. The practice is related to another belief: the child who is born has not yet been shaped. A necklace of large pearls will slim his neck, a belt will slim her waist. Massaging the baby's thighs or applying make-up to the eyelashes are other examples of care that is intended to beautify, to "sculpt" the child.

10 Denko IVORY COAST (The importance of the child)

Singers **Sagna Guire Ramata** and **Thierno Guire Ramata** Language **Bambara**

denko denko
a y'o kɔrɔfɔ n ye
min ka fisa denko ye
a ye kɔrɔ fɔ n ye

The importance of the child
Tell me about it!
What could be more important than a child?
Show me!

Denko is sung by the mothers of the bride or groom on their wedding day while they prepare the young girl and purify her by washing her feet. This song, which is commonly known under a longer version with a different rhythm, can emphasize different moments in daily life. A very joyful song, it immediately sets the tone when the women get together with their children.

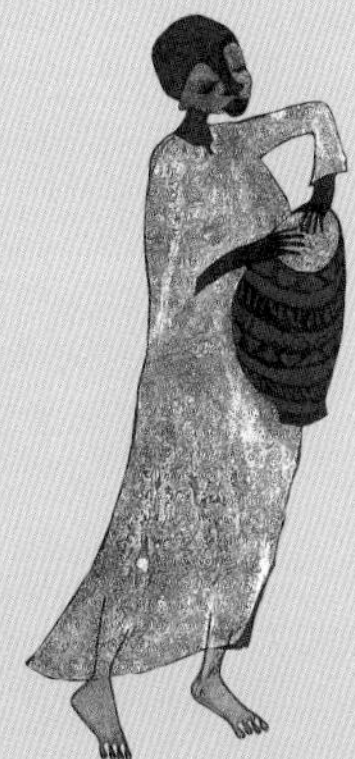

11 Nwou wo' lâ nzi ntâ nseu? CAMEROON (How long has our child been walking?)

Singer Ghislaine Noupa **Language** Bamana

nwou wo' lâ nzi ntâ nseu?	How long has our child been walking?
ntâ ngou' mô tchian tchian	Since last year, hey, hey!
Fifi lâ nzi ntâ nseu?	How long has Fifi been walking?

This nursery rhyme is intended for children who are almost a year old and accompanies them as they take their first steps. The mother places herself in front of the child and sings as she pulls the child towards her. She claps her hands, reaches out to the child, then claps her hands again.

12 Kabuye kanjye RWANDA (My little pebble)

Singers Chantal Habyalimana, Gisèle Candy Nyirabanzi **and** Nadia Uwaliraye **Language** Kinyarwanda

kabuye kanjye, kabuye kanjye ni keza pe	My little pebble, my little pebble is very lovely
enda nawe ukarore, nawe ukarore	Hold it and you look at it too, you look at it too!
ni keza pe	It is very lovely

From the schoolyard to the village streets, everyone knows this song. As in the case of "Eeny, meeny, miny, moe" or "Duck, Duck, Goose," it is used to count and eliminate a member of the group. Sitting in a circle, the children pass a pebble around to the rhythm, and since there is one pebble less than the number of players, the child without a pebble at the end of the song is eliminated.

13 Nkwihoreze **RWANDA (I will comfort you)**

Singers **Chantal Habyalimana, Gisèle Candy Nyirabanzi** and **Nadia Uwaliraye** Language **Kinyarwanda**

nkwihoreze ibyandongo ayiwe, ayiweibyandongo,
nkwihoreze ikobondo humm,
humm, ayiwe ayiwe,
ibyandongo nta joro wandaje ayiwe, ayiweibyandongo,
amanywa, umugoroba humm,
nzaguha amata ayiwe, ayiweibyandongo,
mu cyansi wakunze humm
ngusige amavuta ayiwe, ayiweibyandongo,
umubili uhehere humm
hora hora shenge ayiwe ayiweibyandongo,
nkubwire uduhoza abana humm
nzavuza ubuhuha ayiwe ayiweibyandongo,
ngushyire nyoko wanyu humm
hora muteteli ayiwe ayiweibyandongo,
ngusoromere inkeli humm

I will comfort you, my baby
Take away your sorrow, my little one, my little chick
The nights are calm with you at my side, my baby
The days and evenings with you at my side, my sweet
I will give you milk, my baby, in your favourite jar, my little one
With cream, I will massage you, my baby
And your skin will be so soft, my love
Don't cry, don't cry, sweetheart
I will sing you the most lovely lullabies, my treasure
I will sing you the gentlest lullabies, my baby
And take you to see your beloved aunt, my little one
Don't cry, you are my beloved, my favourite, my baby
I'll pick baskets of strawberries for you, my precious

The mother sings this lively lullaby while tapping on her baby's bottom, reassuring the baby about the good things to come: promises of food, well-being and songs . . . The cream mentioned in the song is made from milk and scented with citronella or mint. As for the strawberries, they are wild and will be gathered in the woods.

14 In ga **GUINEA-CONAKRY (Orphan)**

Singer **Lucienne Yansanne** Language **Susu**

in ga nè na i mou dounigna khonê to mi bè
i baba nè na i mou dounigna khonè to mi bè
Sali Wondé Sali Wondé wo gayé
Sali Wondé dounigna maragnon mama
Sali Wondé Sali Wondé wo bayé
Sali Wondé dounigna maragnon mama

When your mother is alive, you don't know the suffering of life
When your father is alive, you don't know the suffering of life
Sali Wonde, Sali Wonde, our mothers!
Sali Wonde, nothing is eternal
Sali Wonde, Sali Wonde, our fathers!
Sali Wonde, nothing is eternal

This song evokes the sad fate of orphans. Taken in by grandparents, aunts or cousins, they are rarely treated like the other children, particularly within a polygamous family.

15 Faatima Hawwaa **MAURITANIA**

Singers **Haby Sy** and **Ba Sala** Language **Fula**

Bisimillaahi jam mooɗon
– Delluyaa delluyaa delli
Delluyaa dellu! Wullee Yero-Sammba
Delluyaa ! Lament Yero-Samba
Ngoodaami Nokku Tamarooje
Leydi nganndumi ngoowaami
Ɗo cooynotoomi mi jaɓɓee mi jala
Ɓe mbetta leeso e njaganaay
Tufam addee feewnee
Won ko Faatima Hawwaa wii
O wii : « Woyi baaye! Woyi baaye!
Woyi baaye Faatima Hawwaa !
Mo yum mum maayi booraama
Mo baam mum maayi ɓuri bonde »
Won ko gorgol am wiinoo mi
« Mboomri yartaa gosi »
Gorgol am wii : « Mboomri yartaa kafee »
Mbate yum-maa siiwaani
Gorgol am wii : « Mboomri yartaa tufam »
Nde kaawu am jaayii ndee
Wutte moyyo ko gorgol jeyi
Paɗe moyye ko gorgol jeyi
Miin koy gorgol aannii kam!

May peace be with you! – Delluyaa delluyaa delli
I am from the Oasis of Dates
The land where I am well known
When I return to the village, people run out and I'm filled with joy
They unroll the mats, and take out the cushions
And curdled milk is brought to me and prepared for me
Here's what Fâtima Hawwâ said:
She said, "Weep orphan! Weep orphan!
Weep on Fâtima Hawwâ, orphan
Whoever loses their mother is unlucky
Whoever loses their father is even more so."
My paternal aunt told me so
"A young girl doesn't eat millet broth."
My aunt told me: "A young girl does not drink coffee."
Neither broth, nor coffee, unless my mother prepared it
My aunt told me: "A young girl does not drink tufam."
As soon as my uncle passed away
My aunt took his beautiful wide sleeved robe
My aunt took his beautiful shoes
My aunt is very hard on me

This very beautiful lament, in which two voices answer one another (the second supporting the story of the first) brings to mind the Victor Hugo character Cosette in *Les Misérables*. In this case, the orphan, named Fâtima Hawwâ, is raised by an uncle and a sour aunt. Up early, to bed early, working constantly, Fatima does all of the chores. She must go to a distant well to get water. She grinds the millet, does the cooking, braids her aunt's hair. But she receives nothing in return: no clothing, no jewels, not even a thank-you. The misery, destitution and bullying overwhelm her. When the uncle dies, the paternal aunt must take his place. That's why she takes the deceased man's robe and shoes. But instead of taking care of Fâtima, she deprives her of broth, coffee and tufam (curdled milk with water and sugar that is very popular in the Fula area of the Sahel, offered to distinguished guests to honour them). The theme of the orphan girl is recurrent in nursery rhymes, as well as in children's stories. On other occasions, she will be seen contending with a witch disguised as an old woman who introduces her to the secrets of life. These little orphans who are raised so harshly will later become, we are told, people who can deal with the difficulties of life.

16 Makun MALI (Don't cry)

Singer Sylla Mama **Language** Bambara

makun makun Bebe o makun
makun makun Bebe o makun sa
mun de kɛra Bebe la makun
fosi ma kɛ Bebe la makun sa
makun makun Bebe makun
mun de kɛra Bebe la makun
kɔngɔ de bɛ Bebe la i makun sa

Don't cry, don't cry, Baby, don't cry
Don't cry, don't cry, Baby, calm down
What has been done to Baby? Calm down, now
There's nothing wrong with my Baby, don't cry, calm down
Don't cry, don't cry, baby, don't cry
What has been done to Baby? Calm down, now
My Baby is hungry. Don't cry, calm down

This magnificent lullaby is very popular in Mali. It's easy to imagine the mother or the big sister preparing food and inventing words to keep the child patient: she can talk about her work, her relationship with her husband, her friends or even, of course, the child's relationship with his or her surroundings. This is a way of telling children that they can't always get what they want right away. The kora, one of the most beautiful instruments from western Black Africa, brings a particular energy to the basic pattern of the melody on the recording. It can be played as a solo instrument to accompany the tales of the griots.

17 Injangwe yanjye RWANDA (My cat)

Singers Chantal Habyalimana **and** Joanie Bouteloup **Language** Kinyarwanda

injangwe injangwe yanjye irwaye mu mutwe
mama arayigulira ingofero nziza
n'udukweto twiza tra la la la
n'udukweto twiza injangwe injangwe yanjye irwaye mu matwi
mama arayigulira utwuma tw'amatwi
ingofero nziza
n'udukweto twiza tra la la la
n'udukweto twiza injangwe injangwe yanjye irwaye mu maso
mama arayigulira amataratara . . .
injangwe injangwe yanjye irwaye mu gifu
mama arayigulira igikombe cy'amata . . .
injangwe injangwe yanjye noneho yakize
igeze mu muryango ahafata imbeba
iyirya ako kanya tra la la la
iyirya ako kanya

My cat, my cat has a headache
My mommy will buy it a nice hat
And very nice shoes, tra la la
And very nice shoes
My cat, my cat has sore ears
My mommy will buy it earrings, a nice hat
And very nice shoes, tra la la
And very nice shoes
My cat, my cat has sore eyes
My mommy will buy it glasses
My cat, my cat has a stomach ache.
My mommy will buy it a cup of milk
My cat, my cat is healed this time
He comes to the door, he catches a mouse
Raw, he eats it; he eats it raw!

Performed mostly by little girls in the schoolyard, this nursery rhyme is inspired by the French song, "Mon âne" (My donkey). As in the French version, this is a song with gestures and accumulations that exercises the young child's hearing and cognitive memory. The text is almost identical, except that the donkey becomes a cat, the cup of chocolate turns into a glass of milk, and the end provides an additional element to the story: the healed cat catches the mouse!

This recording offers a blend of lyrics with these words in French: Mon âne, mon âne a bien mal à sa tête (My donkey, my donkey has a bad headache), Madame lui fait faire un bonnet pour sa fête (Madame had a bonnet made for him for his birthday), Et des souliers lilas-la-la, et des souliers lilas (And lilac shoes, la, la, and lilac shoes). The song continues by adding new items successively: the ears (a pair of earrings), the eyes (a pair of blue glasses), the nose (a pretty muffler) and, finally, the stomach (a cup of chocolate).

18 Buutulumaani MALI (Buutu player)

Singers Sylla Mama **and** Mama Silamara **Language** Soninke

buutulumaani
buutulumaani, buutulu, kama buutulumaani
kaman kama buutumaani xa buutu
geccere xa ti geccere, kaman geccere xa ti
kaman kama geccere xa ti xa geccere

Buutu players
Talented buutu masters, play buutu!
Buutu players, play buutu, masters!
Geccere players, your turn! Geccere masters, play!
Talented geccere masters, make the geccere ring!

This is a clapping game that mothers play with children or that children play among themselves, sitting in a circle. The leader encourages the children to follow, tapping the rhythm on the ground with his or her hands, palms down first, then palms up. The first one to make a mistake is eliminated. The geccere is a stringed instrument and the buutu is a cow horn into which the men sing when they hunt; it also serves as a powder box for the women who apply black powder to their faces during scarification rites (traditional tattoo practice). Performed by girls, this game also exists in the Wolof language, using onomatopoeias.

19 Sirada la MALI (On the roadside)

Singers Niama Kouyate **and** Sylla Mama **Language** Bambara

ne taara ne taara
ne taara sirada la
n ye wulu ye
n'k'a ka dɔnkili da
a ye dɔnkili da : wow wow
a man gɛlɛn a ma gɛlɛn
n ye misi ye
n k'a ka dɔnkili da
A ye dɔnkili da : nbuu nbuu
n ye jakuma ye
n k'a ka dɔnkili da
a ye dɔnkili da : nyɛn nyɛn
n ye kami ye
n k'a ka dɔnkili da
a ye dɔnkili da : kule kule

I left, I left
I headed down the roadside
I saw a dog, I told it to sing
It sang: woof woof!
It's not hard, it's not hard
I saw a cow, I told it to sing
She sang: moo, moo!
I saw a cat, I told it to sing
It sang: meow, meow!
I saw a guinea fowl, I told it to sing
It sang: coo, coo!

The theme of animals occupies an important place in the repertory of children's songs. Did you know that the Guinea fowl is originally from Africa and that while the chicken clucks or cackles the Guinea fowl screeches? And the cat, in Bambara, can also say "muusi muusi," a sound that is very close to "meow meow" . . . In this song, children are sure to mimic the sounds of domestic animals living in villages or on farms.

20 Tànk loxo nopp **SENEGAL (Leg, arm, ear)**

Singer **Souleymane Mbodj** Language **Wolof**

tank, loxo, nopp, bakkan, baat, bët, gémmiñ, shh!

Leg, arm, ear, nose, neck, eye, mouth, shh!

With this nursery rhyme, all of the body parts are pointed out one by one:

- tank: you tap both hands on your thighs
- loxo: arms crossed, you tap both hands on your upper arms
- nopp: you grab your ears with your fingers
- bakkan: you pinch your nose
- baat: you hold one hand around your neck
- bët: you point your index fingers at both eyes
- gémmiñ: you place your index finger on your mouth

This nursery rhyme, which is very interesting from a psychomotor, rhythmic and sound point of view, involves listing the seven body parts. It can be played faster and faster, seeing who can last the longest.

Although this body knowledge game is difficult at first, it is a lot of fun once the actions are coordinated. The final gesture on the mouth is accompanied by a breath and shows the child the relationship between the inside and the outside of the body. The impressive drum sound on the recording is produced by a talking drum, which is also called an hourglass drum. Cinched in at the middle, it is equipped with strings that apply tension to the two skins of the instrument. It is held under the armpit, and the pressure of the arm on the strings can be used to produce glissandi or, as in this case, pitches and accents inspired by spoken language.

21 N daga an kara **MALI (I went to your house)**

Singers **Sylla Mama** and **Mama Silamara** Language **Soninke**

n daga an kaara n ma an ñi no
n da an renman ñi soose mini
n ti i na in ku i xa bara
n xa da i katu, i xada in katu
n wu, i xa wu
muusuunen tere batte, gajanxullen tere batte
ñoxoli ñoxoli Sanba ñoxoli ñoxoli

I went to your house but you weren't there
Your children were eating couscous with curdled milk
I told them to give me some, but they refused
I beat them, they beat me
I wept, they wept
And pit-a-pat, the fat cat! In and out, the little mouse!
Guili, guili, Samba, guili, guili!

This nursery rhyme is performed in different ways in the countries where the Soninke language is spoken: Mauritania, Mali, Senegal and Gambia. The children sing it while tapping a half gourd (which is also used as a cooking utensil), with the opening turned towards the ground. Others perform it in pairs, face to face. They tap their right hand in the right hand of their partner, and their left hand in the left to the rhythm. Then each partner tickles the other's neck. The mother can also tap her baby's palm, then mimic the steps of the cat and the mouse running along the baby's arm up to the armpit or neck. It should be noted that Samba is the name given to the second boy in a family. In fact, each child is given a name based on his or her birth order, as is common in many other African countries.

22 Tutu gbo̱vi TOGO (My love)

Singers **Lucie Da Silvera** and **Kelly Da Silvera** Language **Mina**

tutu gbo̱vi tutu gbo̱vi	My love, my love
nana mu lé ahuéa méwo	Mommy is not home
tata mu lé ahuéa méwo	Daddy is not home
aoh djédjé vinyé bónu bonu kpo	Oh! My little love, stop crying
mé kèyé poé ma	Who hit you?
pauluvi ya	Was it Little Paul?
tutan né ma poé nawo	Spit it out so I can hit him back
aoh djédjé vinyé mugba fa avio	Don't cry, my love
aoh djédjé vinyé bónu bónu kpo	My dear, stop crying

The question "Who hit you?" recurs frequently in many African lullabies. When a baby cries, it is common to ask it who could have hurt it. In Togo or Senegal, the child will be asked to spit into the adult's hand to authorize the adult to take vengeance. Thus, if the child fell, the adult will hit the ground, if he/she ran into a wall, the adult will hit the wall . . . The effect is immediate: this magical gesture (like blowing where it hurts, in other cultures) causes the child to forget about the pain.

23 Îtä Zâke CENTRAL AFRICAN REPUBLIC (Frère Jacques)

Singers **Marilyne Seredouma** and **Juliet Hoarau** Language **Sango**

îtä Zâke!	Brother John,
mo längö?	Are you sleeping?
ngbonga apîka awe	Morning bells are ringing.
mo zîngo!	Wake up!

"Frère Jacques" is beyond a doubt the most exported French song. In the Republic of Central Africa, where it was effectively taught in the French schools in Bangui, the capital, it was quickly translated into Sango, the most commonly spoken language in the country. The name "Jacques" is written Zâke regardless of the pronunciation and "îtä" means brother or sister, without any religious connotation. This famous canon no longer evokes monastic life in this case but a more prosaic daily life: John, my brother, it's time to get up! Used for the musical accompaniment, the xylophone, called bala in Guinea and Mali, and kâlângbâ in the Central African Republic, is made up of a series of tuned wooden blades that are struck with mallets. This ancient instrument, which is very widespread in Black Africa, may be played on numerous occasions by healers, griots or other musicians.

23 Awe bebëe! (It's over, baby)
CENTRAL AFRICAN REPUBLIC

Singers **Marilyne Seredouma** and **Juliet Hoarau** Language **Sango**

awe bebëe!
mamâ ague na ngû
tî tö ngû, fadë lo 'ke gä
mbâ tî mo bebëe apîka mo
sï mo toto sô, toto äpë o!

It's over, baby! Mommy has gone to the river
To get some water; she'll be back soon
It's a baby, a baby like you who hit you
That's why you're crying, don't cry sweetheart

This lullaby is sung to babies, carried in a sling on the mother's belly when he or she is very young, then on her back until the child is walking. It is common to hear little girls sing this song to their dolls. Referring to a possible assault, the adult reassures the child. Sometimes an older baby can be particularly jealous of a smaller baby and may hit it. Even if the assault is not real, it is important to find the words to express children's sadness or simply their fatigue, which sometimes overwhelms them.

24 Aayaa yimbéy SENEGAL

Singer **Souleymane Mbodj** Language **Wolof**

aayaa yimbéy
aayaa yóo Sàmba Wore doom yimbéy!
kaala ak kurus,
Aayaa yóo, Sàmba Wore, son, yimbéy!
satala ak borom
yaay bóoy bañuma ko
dama koo ragal
yaay!

Aayaa yimbéy
Aayaa yóo, Sàmba Wore, son, yimbéy
With his turban and his string of beads
With his satala*
Mommy dearest, it's not that I hate him
But, I'm afraid of him!
Mommy!

* kettle used for ablutions

The melody of this very old song is also used with other, more recent words that mean: if you're thirsty, you must drink, if you thirst for knowledge, you must learn.

25 Bo bo bo bo GUINEA-CONAKRY

Singer **Lucienne Yansanne** Language **Susu**

bo bo bo bo
bo bo wama khi féra
khignè nou mouna kna fiama
bo bo bo bo

Bo bo bo bo
Baby is crying for milk
But I don't have any to give him
Bo bo bo bo

Particularly well-known in the Basse-Côte region of Guinea-Conakry, this lullaby is sung by the mother, sisters or other family members. The singer taps the baby's back or bottom; lying beside the baby, the mother can also caress its head.

26 Dunga CENTRAL AFRICAN REPUBLIC

Singer **Marilyne Seredouma** Language **Sango**

mo bâa Dunga, mo mä gô tî âzo sô
ë dutï na mo, ë yë bîâ na mo o!
mo bâa Dunga, mo mä gô tî âzo sô
ë dutï na mo, ë sâra ngîâ na mo
na lâ nî sô mo gä na ndo tî ë
mbï bâa gï mo, na mabôko tî mbï e!
na lâ nî sô mo gä na ndo tî ë
mbï dutï wâlï, mamâ tî mo ôko

You see, Dunga, listen to these people's voices
We live with you, we sing for you, ho!
You see, Dunga, listen to these people's voices
We live with you, we play with you
The day that you came to our house
I saw only you, in my arms, hey!
The day that you came to our house
I became a woman, your only mother!

The name Dunga means "Take your strength from nature." This lullaby is a poetic greeting to the newborn child. It focuses on the place each individual holds within the group. The entire community makes sure the newborn is welcome.

27 Usumani ka dundunnin MALI
(Ousamane's little drum)

Singers **Niama Kouyate** and **Sylla Mama** Language **Bambara**

usumani ka dundunnin kan bɔra ka taa wale
n'i ye dɔnkili da ne na tɛkɛrɛ f'i ye f'i ka taga Farafinna
anh ne fa waalen
anh o b'a diya sa
anh ne ba waalen
anh o b'a diya sa
seleku seleku bɛ dɔn na
seleku seleku n'a nyanabɔ
karatu karatu bɛ dɔn na
karatu karatu n'a nyɛnabɔ
ka taa n kale cɛmisɛn
ka taa n kale sungurunw
Ka taa n kale denmisɛnw
ka taa n kale sungurunw

The little heralding drum, Ousamane's little drum sounded
If you sing I'll clap my hands until you arrive in Africa
Oh, my father is gone
Oh, that's so good!
Oh, my mother is gone
Oh, that's so good!
Selekou selekou, dance!
Selekou selekou will take care of it
Karatou karatou, dance!
Karatou karatou will take care of it
And you, young people, I am taking up the challenge!
And you, girls, I am taking up the challenge!
And you, children, I am taking up the challenge!
And you, girls, I am taking up the challenge!

This celebration song is sung by young people when their parents are absent. Ousmane plays his heralding drum to make the girls dance. But, it is also a children's song since mothers can use it to make them jump in their arms or when carrying them on their backs, to lull them or calm them by dancing to the rhythm. In Africa, calming children often involves movement; little three-year-olds accompany the song by clapping their hands.

28 Gato gato RWANDA (The smallest)

Singers **Chantal Habyalimana, Gisèle Candy Nyirabanzi** and **Nadia Uwaliraye** Language **Kinyarwanda**

gato gato we
gato gato mu bakobwa b'iwacu
ngwino urare shenge ngwino urare we
ngwino urare mu gitondo urataha
nguwo araje ni umukobwa useka neza
nyampinga mumurebe nguwo yaje
ngaho seruka shenge nyiraguhirwa
umukobwa uhiriwe n'Imana
nguwo shenge nyamuberwa n'inkindi we
ngaho seruka ugaragaze uwo mubyimba

Little one, you are the prettiest girl of all!
Come and spend the night with us
You can go home tomorrow
Here she is, the young girl with the beautiful smile
Look at her, the one we can count on
Show yourself, we're waiting, you who is destined for happiness,
you, God's princess
Here's the beautiful one, well dressed, show yourself,
make your beautiful silhouette dance
Here she is, the beautiful gazelle, she's ready to liven up the evening
Show yourself, you are the pearl of our house, a white pearl,
a most precious gem

This dancing game, which is very widespread in Rwanda, is performed by a group of six to ten girls, from a young age to adolescence. One of them starts doing a certain step. A soloist describes her physical and moral qualities and the choir echoes this. Then each person finds a different dance.

29 Wá wá wá wá CONGO (Quietly, listen to me)

Singers **Marie-Cécile Maloumbi Mata** and **Jean-Marie Bolangassa** Language **Kikongo**

wá wá wá wá
éh! mwânâ ndila
wá wá wá wá
eh mwânâ ndila éh máma !
yambúla bidilu bya kúmámánda bi byó
bi yána bubélu
yambúla bídílu bya kútátánda bí byó
bi yána tiya é é
mwânâ ulémbólo ná táta
tála lúsámbúlwálélé
mwânâ wákónda táta, mámánda
tála bánsúngi yátóbo

Quietly, listen to me
My child, don't cry
Don't cry, my child
Mommy is here
Don't cry, don't cry for your mother
You will get a fever
Don't cry, don't cry for your father
You will have a temperature
The child torn from his father, this is his prayer
The child who has lost father and mother
You, his family, take care of him!

This lullaby for orphans is divided into two distinct parts. The refrain is known by everyone and the verses provide an opportunity for each mother to improvise for her child. She asks the families to support the children who have no parents, to ensure their future, provide their food and educate them. Known throughout the Congo and in Angola, it varies according to the region. In Brazzaville and Kinshasa, it is performed in Lingala, the official language of the capitals.

Tunisia
Morocco
Algeria
Libyan Arab Jamahiriya
Egypt
Western Sahara
Mauritania
Mali
Niger
Chad
Eritrea
Sudan
Cape Verde
Senegal
Burkina Faso
Gambia
Djibouti
Guinea
Nigeria
Ethiopia
Ghana
Sierra Leone
Ivory Coast
Benin
Togo
Central African Republic
Somalia
Liberia
Cameroon
Equatorial Guinea
Uganda
Kenya
Congo
Gabon
Rwanda
Republic of the Congo
Burundi
Seychelle
Tanzania
Comoros
Mayotte
Angola
Malawi
Zambia
Zimbabwe
Madagascar
Namibia
Botswana
Reunion
Mozambique
Swaziland
Lesotho
South Africa

Retaining 11 languages to express the repertory of African lullabies and nursery rhymes could appear very oversimplified considering that linguists have identified more than 2,000 languages. However, most of them are among the 30 most commonly used languages in Black Africa. In their homelands, African children are often exposed to several languages: the language of the ethnic group to which they belong (either that of the father or the mother, depending on whether the ethnic group is patrilinear or matrilinear), which will be the language of the earliest lullabies, then the language their parents use with neighbours of other ethnicities, which may be regional or national and, lastly, the language learned at school. Their repertory of lullabies, nursery rhymes and songs reproduces this broad palette!

The impact of French colonization is still evident in Black Africa. Thus, in the homelands of our performers, the official language and the one that is learned in school is still French. Only Kinyarwanda in Rwanda and Sango in the Central African Republic are acknowledged as official languages in the same respect as French. This influence is also found in nursery rhymes.

With the exception of Wolof and Fula, all are tone-based languages. Tones correspond to the different pitches of the voice on syllables and imply changes in meaning. They are most often indicated by diacriticals (accents, diereses, or dashes). The transcriptions collected from linguists follow the most common criteria. The international phonetic alphabet, which includes, for certain languages, certain special characters, is the one most often used. For example, a double vowel indicates a prolonged sound, a double consonant indicates a stronger articulation and certain series of consonants are to be considered as phonic units (e.g., mp, mb, mc in Wolof are pronounced as a single consonant).

The languages often extend beyond the borders and are spoken in the following countries:

Bambara
Mali, Ivory Coast

Bamana
Cameroon

Fula
Senegal, Mauritania, Guinea-Conakry, Mali, Burkina Faso, Niger, Nigeria, Cameroon, Central African Republic, Chad

Kikongo
Democratic Republic of the Congo, Congo, Angola

Kinyarwanda
Rwanda

Lingala
Democratic Republic of the Congo, Congo

Mina
Togo

Soninke
Mali, Mauritania, Senegal

Sango
Central African Republic

Susu
Guinea-Conakry

Wolof
Senegal, Gambia

Song selection, notes and vocal coordination **Chantal Grosléziat** Illustrations **Élodie Nouhen** Record Producer **Paul Mindy** Musical arrangement **Xavier Desandre-Navarre, Jean-Christophe Hoarau** and **Paul Mindy** Recorded at **Studio Toupie** and **Studio Desandre** Mixed and mastered by **Philippe Kadosch** at **Multicrea** Graphic Design **Stephan Lorti** for **Haus Design**

Singers **Jean-Marie Bolangassa, Lucie Da Silvera, Marilyne Seredouma, Sagna Guire Ramata, Chantal Habyalimana, Niama Kouyate, Marie-Cécile Maloumbi Mata, Sylla Mama, Souleymane Mbodj, Ghislaine Noupa, Aminata Seck, Haby Sy, Lucienne Yansanne, Ba Sala, Joanie Bouteloup, Gisèle Candy Nyirabanzi, Nadia Uwaliraye**

Children's voices **James Da Silvera, Kelly Da Silvera, Tracy Da Silvera, Thierno Guire Ramata, Juliet Hoarau, Uriel Koukou Cissoko, Mama Silamara, Anaïs Mwinda Mata, Clarisse Mata, Emmanuel Victor Mata**

Musicians **Djéli Moussa Conde** kora **Jean-Christophe Hoarau** guitar, bass, cavaquinho **Xavier Desandre-Navarre** and **Paul Mindy** percussion, flute, kalimba

Translations **Ismaël Maïga** and **Keita Sokona** (Bambara), **Ghislaine** and **David Noupa** (Bamana), **Souleymane Baldé** and **Mohamadou Aliou** (Fula), **Léa Kathona** (Kikongo and Lingala), **Chantal Habyalimana** (Kinyarwanda), **Sylvana Ablavi Anthony** (Mina), **Marcel Diki-Kidiri** (Sango), **Mamadou Djimera** (Soninke), **Aboubacar Sidiki Mara** (Susu), **Jean-Léopold Diouf** (Wolof), **Services d'édition Guy Connolly** (French to English)

Aknowledgements **Nana Taka, Solange Edoukou, Kebba Sousoko, Malamin** [illegible] **Kine Dia, Mélanie Valmary, Cheron Aminata, Itela Bosange, Michel Gnivo Correa** [illegible] **i, Suzie Platiel, Marie-George Rigaut, Évelyne Resmond-Wenz, Marie Lau**[illegible] **Ba, Henri Samba, Diallo Fade, Françoise Diep, Abou Fall, Dia Fatoumata, R**[illegible] **Nja Kwa**

Published with the support of the Fonds d'Action Sociale and the Centre national du livre, Pari[illegible]

www.thesecretmountain.com
©℗ **2011 The Secret Mountain (Folle Avoine Productions)**

ISBN-10 2-923163-79-6 / ISBN-13 978-2-923163-79-6 First published in France by Didier Je[illegible] No part of this publication may be reproduced or transmitted in any form or by any means, electronic or [illegible] ing or any information storage and retrieval system, without permission in writing from the publisher. Print[illegible] o).